rockschool®

Drums Grade 3

*Performance pieces, technical exercises and in-depth guidance
for Rockschool examinations*

All accompanying and supporting audio can be downloaded from: *www.rslawards.com/downloads*

Input the following code when prompted: **6VDSTFE7AS**

For more information, turn to page 4

www.rslawards.com

Acknowledgements

Published by Rockschool Ltd. © 2012
Catalogue Number RSK051222
ISBN: 978-1-908920-21-8
7 August 2014 | Errata details can be found at *www.rslawards.com*

AUDIO
Recorded at Fisher Lane Studios
Produced and engineered by Nick Davis
Assistant engineer and Pro Tools operator Mark Binge
Mixed and mastered at Langlei Studios
Mixing and additional editing by Duncan Jordan
Supporting Tests recorded by Duncan Jordan and Kit Morgan
Mastered by Duncan Jordan
Executive producers James Uings, Jeremy Ward and Noam Lederman

MUSICIANS
James Arben, Joe Bennett, Jason Bowld, Larry Carlton, Stuart Clayton, Andy Crompton, Neel Dhorajiwala, Fergus Gerrand,
Charlie Griffiths, Felipe Karam, Kishon Khan, Noam Lederman, DJ Harry Love, Dave Marks, Kit Morgan, Jon Musgrave,
Jake Painter, Richard Pardy, Ross Stanley, Stuart Ryan, Carl Sterling, Henry Thomas, Camilo Tirado, Simon Troup,
James Uings, Steve Walker, Chris Webster, Norton York, Nir Z

PUBLISHING
Fact Files written by Luke Aldridge, Jason Bowld, Neel Dhorajiwala, Stephen Lawson, Noam Lederman and David West
Walkthroughs written by Noam Lederman
Music engraving and book layout by Simon Troup and Jennie Troup of Digital Music Art
Proof and copy editing by Noam Lederman, Claire Davies, Stephen Lawson, Simon Pitt and James Uings
Publishing administration by Caroline Uings
Cover design by Philip Millard

SYLLABUS
Syllabus director: Jeremy Ward
Instrumental specialists: Stuart Clayton, Noam Lederman and James Uings
Special thanks to: Brad Fuller and Georg Voros.

SPONSORSHIP
Noam Lederman plays Mapex Drums, PAISTE cymbals and uses Vic Firth Sticks
Rockschool would like to thank the following companies for donating instruments used in the cover artwork

PRINTING
Printed and bound in the United Kingdom by Caligraving Ltd

DISTRIBUTION
Exclusive Distributors: Music Sales Ltd

CONTACTING ROCKSCHOOL
www.rslawards.com
Telephone: +44 (0)845 460 4747
Email: *info@rslawards.com*

Table of Contents

Introductions & Information

Rockschool Grade Pieces

Technical Exercises

Supporting Tests

Additional Information

Welcome to Rockschool Drums Grade 3

Welcome to Drums Grade 3

Welcome to the Rockschool Drums Grade 3 pack. This book and the accompanying downloadable audio contain everything to play drums at this grade. In the book you will find the exam scores in drum notation. The downloadable audio includes full stereo mixes of each tune, backing tracks to play along to for practice and spoken two bar count-ins to both the full mixes and backing track versions of the songs. There are two backing tracks of each song: one with a click and one without. You can choose which one to play along with in the exam.

Drum Exams

At each grade, you have the option of taking one of two different types of examination:

- **Grade Exam:** a Grade Exam is a mixture of music performances, technical work and tests. You prepare three pieces (two of which may be Free Choice Pieces) and the contents of the Technical Exercise section. This accounts for 75% of the exam marks. The other 25% consists of: *either* a Sight Reading *or* an Improvisation & Interpretation test (10%), a pair of instrument specific Ear Tests (10%) and finally you will be asked five General Musicianship Questions (5%). The pass mark is 60%.

- **Performance Certificate:** In a Performance Certificate you play five pieces. Up to three of these can be Free Choice Pieces. Each song is marked out of 20 and the pass mark is 60%.

Book Contents

The book is divided into a number of sections. These are:

- **Exam Pieces:** in this book you will find six specially commissioned pieces of Grade 3 standard. Each of these is preceded by a *Fact File*. Each Fact File contains a summary of the song, its style, tempo, key and technical features, along with a list of the musicians who played on it. The song itself is printed on two pages. Immediately after each song is a *Walkthrough*. This covers the song from a performance perspective, focusing on the technical issues you will encounter. Each song comes with a full mix version and a backing track. Both versions have spoken count-ins at the beginning. Please note that any solos played on the full mix versions are indicative only.

- **Technical Exercises:** you should prepare the exercises set in this grade as indicated. There is also a Fill test that should be practised and played to the backing track.

- **Supporting Tests and General Musicianship Questions:** in Drums Grade 3 there are three supporting tests – *either* a Sight Reading *or* an Improvisation & Interpretation test and two Ear Tests – and a set of General Musicianship Questions (GMQs) asked at the end of each exam. Examples of the types of tests likely to appear in the exam are printed in this book. Additional test examples of both types of test and the GMQs can be found in the Rockschool *Companion Guide To Drums*.

- **Additional Information:** finally, you will find information on exam procedures, marking schemes, and the full notation and backing track of a piece from the next grade as a taster.

Audio

In addition to the Grade book, we have also provided audio in the form of backing tracks (minus drums, with *and* without click) and examples (including drums) for both the pieces and the supporting tests where applicable. This can be downloaded from RSL directly at *www.rslawards.com/downloads*

You will need to input this code when prompted: **6VDSTFE7AS**

The audio files are supplied in MP3 format. Once downloaded you will be able to play them on any compatible device.

Syllabus Guide

All candidates should read the accompanying syllabus guide when using this grade book. This can be downloaded from the RSL website: *www.rslawards.com*

SONG TITLE: OVERRATED
GENRE: ALTERNATIVE ROCK
TEMPO: 155 BPM

TECH FEATURES: SYNCOPATED PUSHES
16ᵀᴴ-NOTE ROLLS
FLAMS BETWEEN DRUMS

COMPOSERS: BOB GRACEFUL
& KUNG FU DRUMMER

PERSONNEL: STUART RYAN (GTR)
HENRY THOMAS (BASS)
NOAM LEDERMAN (DRUMS)

OVERVIEW

'Overrated' is an alternative rock track in the style of bands like Foo Fighters, Biffy Clyro and Twin Atlantic. It features flams, 16th-note fills and syncopated pushes among its techniques.

STYLE FOCUS

Alternative rock can be a relentless, driving style for drummers and when accents and grooves are loud they are played with absolute purpose. For instance, it is common for a drummer to crash in a groove to create the biggest lift possible in a chorus section. Flam driven accents and grooves played on the snare are common. They are trademarks of Dave Grohl, who drummed with Nirvana and occasionally with his band Foo Fighters and Queens Of The Stone Age. Always have a 'toolbox' of fills on standby because a variety of 16th-note rolls are essential for playing between spacious guitar stabs. Conviction is everything in this style, so play it like you mean it.

THE BIGGER PICTURE

Foo Fighter's frontman Grohl has been central to the development of this branch of alternative rock.

While still playing drums with Nirvana he began working on demo tapes that lay the bedrock for the Foo Fighters' eponymous first album. Grohl formed the band (which was originally intended to be a solo effort) in Seattle, 1994, following the suicide of Nirvana frontman and guitarist Kurt Cobain. Early Foo Fighters' records retained the quiet-loud dynamic of Nirvana's music while revealing the natural melody of Grohl's songwriting. This combination of rock and melody has led to multi-platinum sales and to Foo Fighters becoming one of the foremost acts in rock.

The influence of Foo Fighters is most obvious in two contemporary alt rock groups, both of whom happen to come from the West of Scotland: Biffy Clyro and Twin Atlantic.

RECOMMENDED LISTENING

Foo Fighters have been releasing music since 1995, adding up to a huge back catalogue. Some of their finest tracks can be found on their *Greatest Hits* (2009). Biffy Clyro's last album, *Only Revolutions* (2009), was their commercial breakthrough but their previous record, *Puzzle* (2007), bears a more obvious Foo Fighters influence. The latest album by Twin Atlantic, *Free* (2011), was the subject of much critical acclaim and is testament to Grohl's enduring legacy.

Overrated

Bob Graceful & Kung Fu Drummer

Walkthrough

A Section (Bars 1–8)
This section is based on a 3:3:2 groove using flams on drums, fills in bars 4 and 8, and a syncopated push in bar 8.

Bar 2 | *3:3:2 groove*
This 3:3:2 groove consists of eight eighth notes divided into three groups: three, three and two eighth notes. The flams are placed on the first eighth note of each group and the bass drum fills in between. Ensure that all of the eighth notes are even and played in a continuous way. Experiment with the sticking and choose the option that feels most comfortable according to your technique (Fig. 1).

Bar 3 | *Flams between drums*
All snare flams in this section are played on one drum. However, in bar 3 there is one stroke on beat four that includes a flam between the medium and floor toms. The balance in this flam should be as notated (i.e. a grace note on the medium tom followed by the main stroke on the floor tom). Ensure that the flow of the groove is not affected here.

Bar 8 | *Syncopated push*
After the initial crash hit on the first beat, there is a snare on the second beat and another crash on the offbeat of the second beat. The crash cymbal played on the offbeat makes this part of the bar more accented than usual. This is known as syncopation.

B Section (Bars 9–16)
The first main groove is introduced in the form of quarter-note crashes, backbeat snare and a busy bass drum pattern. In bar 16, a fill leads into the next section.

Bar 9 | *Crash led groove*
This groove is common in alternative rock and needs to be played evenly. Use a steady, consistent motion on the crash so that you can focus on the accuracy of the bass drum and snare. Set up the crash in the most comfortable place in order to achieve fluency.

C Section (Bars 17–28)
This is the second main groove of the piece, and consistent balance and sound production are vital.

Bar 18 | *Syncopated snare groove*
The snare is played on the offbeat of the second beat and on the fourth beat. The snare that lands on the offbeat is syncopated. Ensure you can play the full groove accurately and comfortably before moving forward. Next, focus on the balance between the drums and the overall sound you produce. Making sure the eighth notes on the floor tom are even and consistent will lead to a more convincing sound.

D Section (Bars 29–40)
In this section there are four bars with crash hits and fills followed by an eight-bar guitar solo.

Bar 29 | *16th note fills*
The crashes on beat one and the offbeat of beat two support the guitar and bass. Therefore, these must be accurately synchronised with the track. Between the crash hits there are 16th note fills on the snare drum. Hit the snare drum head in the middle and use alternate sticking (starting with your right) to achieve a consistent and convincing sound (Fig. 2).

Bars 33–40 | *Guitar solo accompaniment*
For this part you will need to develop the groove according to the style, your personal interpretation and the other instruments used on the backing track. The development created by the drums is meant to support the soloist and provide an exciting foundation for the improvisation.

E Section (Bars 41–53)
The E section starts with the same groove introduced in the B section. It intensifies from bar 45, thanks to the addition of extra snare drums. In bars 49–52 you are required to play some of your own improvised fills as directed.

Bar 49 | *Fill*
When the word fill appears in the notation above any bar with slashed notes, play your own improvised fill. This should be accurate and in keeping with the style of the piece.

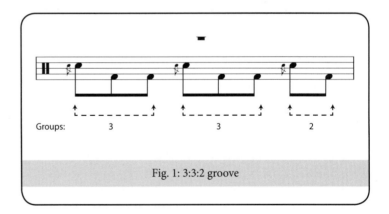

Fig. 1: 3:3:2 groove

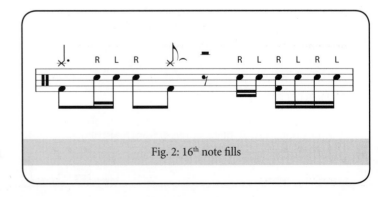

Fig. 2: 16th note fills

Old Bones Blues

SONG TITLE: OLD BONES BLUES

GENRE: BLUES

TEMPO: 115 BPM

TECH FEATURES: SWUNG GROOVES
TRIPLET FILLS
OPEN/CLOSED HI-HAT

COMPOSER: KIT MORGAN

PERSONNEL: STUART RYAN (GTR)
HENRY THOMAS (BASS)
NOAM LEDERMAN (DRUMS)
PETE COGGINS (HARP)

OVERVIEW

'Old Bones Blues' is a blues track inspired by the 12-bar blues formula. The piece features a steady swung feel and eighth-note triplet rolls that crescendo to complement the resolving 12-bar blues cycle.

STYLE FOCUS

To play blues convincingly, the first thing you have to learn is how to swing. The swing feel in the basic shuffle pattern is created by playing the first and third triplets on every beat. Missing the second triplet on every beat gives the shuffle its unique feel and flow. This pattern is played on the hi-hat or ride cymbal, while the snare is played on the backbeat and the bass drum primarily holds beats one and three in each bar. Various combinations of triplet rhythms can be used for fills around the kit. Dynamics are important because blues can feature sections that drop to low volumes and then erupt into lively sections. This is often done to reflect the emotional range of the lyric.

THE BIGGER PICTURE

Blues began in America's Deep South at the end of the 19th century among African American communities. It is one of the most important styles of music because it has influenced a myriad of others including metal, jazz, pop, R&B, hard rock, and even folk and country.

As the genre's name suggests, blues lyrics are often plaintive in character. Common themes include heartbreak or financial and social adversity, but the music of some blues tracks can contrast wonderfully with a lively sound and burst of energy. Quite often the 12-bar formula uses a repeated, sung phrase in each verse that can change in emotional intensity.

Guitar, drums, bass and vocals provide the standard blues instrumentation and are often accompanied by harmonica. Bottleneck slides, which are slid up and down the strings to produce a distinctive 'legato' sound, are also popular among blues guitarists.

RECOMMENDED LISTENING

To gain a broad understanding of blues, start by checking out any 'best of' packages by the godfathers of electric blues Muddy Waters and John Lee Hooker. For modern, commercial blues the albums *Continuum* (2006) and *Battle Studies* (2009) by John Mayer feature the excellent drumming of Steve Jordan who has also played with Eric Clapton.

Old Bones Blues

Kit Morgan

Guitar Solo (8 bars)

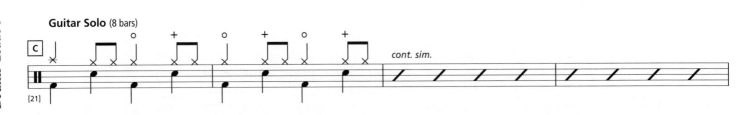

[25]

Develop

[29]

D

[33]

[37]

[40]

[43]

[46]

Drums Grade 3

Walkthrough

A Section (Bars 1–4)
The introduction to 'Old Bones Blues' consists of a basic swung groove with a triplet fill at the end of bar 4.

Bar 1 | *Swung groove*
There is a rhythmic indication above the groove in this bar, which says that two eighth notes are equal to a quarter and eighth-note triplet. This is typical of much blues and will apply to the whole drum part. The best way to understand this rhythmic change is to first replace the eighth notes with triplets and then omit the second triplet in each group of three to achieve the swung groove. The same concept is used in swing beats that are common in jazz (Fig. 1).

B Section (Bars 5–20)
Play the stabs in the first eight bars while holding your hi-hat foot on the backbeat. A swung hi-hat groove comes in after the preparation fill in bar 12.

Bars 5–10 | *Hitting the stabs*
It is common for the drummer to hold a hi-hat foot backbeat while accenting the stabs. In this section, the stabs are played on beat one, the offbeat of beats three and four. After successfully co-ordinating this with your hi-hat foot, take a close look at the voicing used.

Bar 12 | *Triplet fill and crescendo*
Playing alternate sticking triplets with your hands while holding quarter note bass drums will help strengthen your hand-foot co-ordination. It will also assist you in performing even strokes on the snare and tom, and creating the required dynamic change. This dynamic change is known as crescendo, a common music term which means gradually getting louder (Fig. 2).

Bar 13 | *Swinging the hi-hat eighth notes*
The eighth notes on the hi-hat must be swung throughout. Forgetting to swing the eighths will lead to a standard rock groove instead of this exciting and jumpy blues beat.

C Section (Bars 21–32)
Now you have the opportunity to vary stylistically and/or develop the drum part according to your interpretation.

Bar 22 | *Swing on hi-hat*
This pattern is the basic jazz swing groove. It involves reliable hand-foot co-ordination and excellent timing. Adding the backbeat snare and bass on beats one and three makes the groove more appropriate for this blues style. Ensure that your foot always remains in contact with the pedal and your posture is balanced while performing this hi-hat pattern.

Bar 23 | *Cont. sim.*
Cont. sim. means you should continue in a similar way but vary the pattern slightly. Some ideas for variations are extra crashes, bass and snare drum variations and effective fills.

Bar 29 | *Development*
This should be more intense than the cont. sim. section and, ideally, treated as a drum solo or fills around what is played on the track. Remember that any improvised section needs to sound fluent, effortless and convincing.

D Section (Bars 33–48)
The groove in this section is similar to the one introduced previously in the A section.

Bars 33–47 | *Sound production: ride cymbal*
To achieve a clear ring from the ride cymbal, try playing with the tip of your drum stick and hit the cymbal in the area that is half way between the bell and the edge of the cymbal. Hitting the same area of a cymbal will produce a more consistent sound.

Bars 47–48 | *Crossover fill*
A fill played across the bar line is most commonly referred to as a crossover fill. Play the eighth-note triplets with confidence to give the sound a consistent feel and maintain a steady pulse. The last two crashes in bar 48 follow the guitar and bass parts, so listen to the track and synchronise accurately with them.

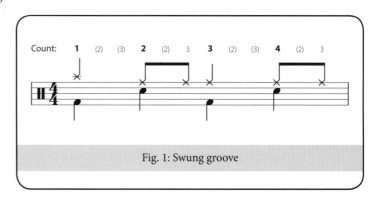

Fig. 1: Swung groove

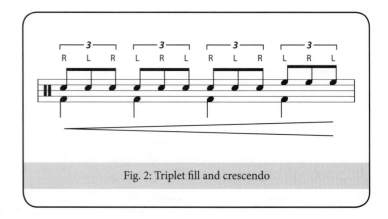

Fig. 2: Triplet fill and crescendo

SONG TITLE: INDECISIVE
GENRE: POP PUNK
TEMPO: 155 BPM

TECH FEATURES: FAST PUNK GROOVES
16TH NOTE FILLS
IMPROVISATION

COMPOSER: JAMES UINGS

PERSONNEL: STUART RYAN (GTR)
HENRY THOMAS (BASS)
NOAM LEDERMAN (DRUMS)

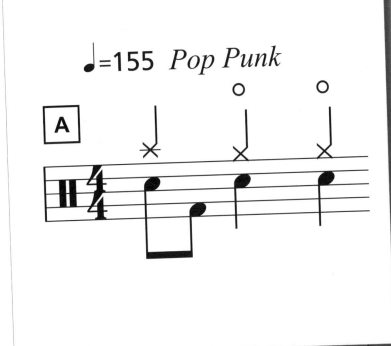

OVERVIEW

'Indecisive' is a pop punk track that pays homage to the bands Blink-182 and Sum 41, in particular to Blink-182's drummer Travis Barker. The track features steady, solid grooving with controlled fills and accents that complement the rhythm guitar riffs.

STYLE FOCUS

This style of pop punk boasts colour and intelligence in the drumming, largely thanks to the influence of Barker. A little more thought and control is needed in the grooves and fills because various open hi-hat accents are often used with other embellishments such as the occasional cymbal bell played on various syncopated beats and fills. This style of pop punk leaves more room for the drummer to be creative, so simply blazing around the kit in 16th notes won't do. Carefully placed accents and broken 16th note fills will suit better and add further excitement to the music.

THE BIGGER PICTURE

Blink-182 formed in California in the early 1990s, as Green Day and The Offspring were beginning

to achieve global success with their own pop punk sounds. As a power trio, Blink-182's sound leaves a generous amount of space for Barker to show off his drumming talents, which have been used to great effect on their various studio albums. The band released albums throughout the 1990s and 2000s, including the chart-topping *Take Off Your Pants And Jacket* in 2001.

Later on, Sum 41 came to prominence at the turn of the millennium as a pop punk group that incorporated elements of metal into their sound. Their *All Killer, No Filler* (2001) album documents the group at their most pop punk.

RECOMMENDED LISTENING

The album *Enema Of The State* by Blink-182 (1999) is a good place to start with pop punk. Tracks such as 'All The Small Things' and 'Adam's Song' will educate you on Barker's lively, colourful style. *Take Off Your Pants And Jacket* features some speedy drumming from Barker and the songs 'Rollercoaster' and 'First Date' contain some creative fills. Another band to take note of for this style of drumming, courtesy of Steve Jocz, is Sum 41. Their song 'Fat Lip' is the band's most successful to date and is available on their debut album *All Killer, No Filler*.

Indecisive

James Uings

♩=155 *Pop Punk*

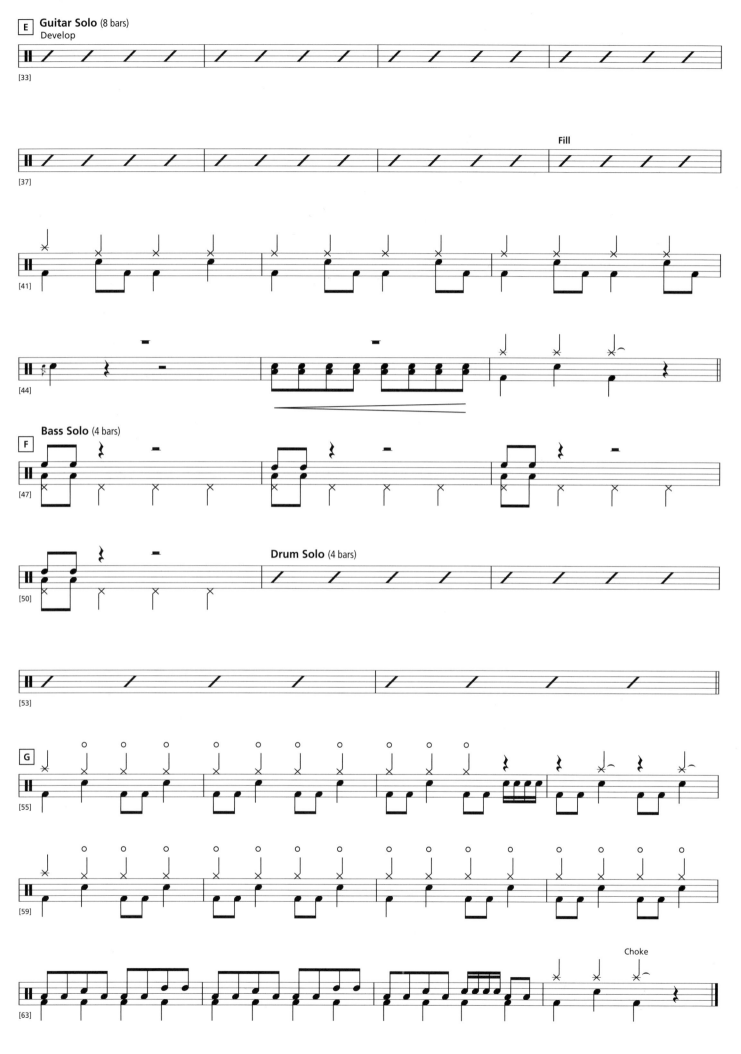

Walkthrough

A Section (Bars 1–8)
The beginning features an uptempo punk groove with open hi-hats, snare on every beat and a varied bass drum pattern.

Bar 1 | *Open hi-hat groove*
The open hi-hat must sound even in this groove. In order to achieve this, your hi-hat foot must remain steady and in constant contact with the pedal. The bass drum variations should be synchronised precisely with the guitar pattern.

B Section (Bars 9–16)
In this section the hi-hat should be closed. Pay attention to the rests and maintain the full length of each rest.

C Section (Bars 17–24)
The groove develops to quarter-note open hi-hats and fills.

Bar 20 | *Crash/snare hit*
In this bar, there are crash/snare strokes on the backbeat. Co-ordinate the movement of your hands accurately: leave your left hand on the snare and shift your right from the hi-hat to the crash. These hits should be synchronised precisely with the guitar and bass patterns (Fig. 1).

D Section (Bars 25–32)
This is a reprise of section B with a few added eighth note bass drums.

E Section (Bars 33–46)
The guitar solo fills the first eight bars of this section and you must develop a drum part in keeping with the style. In bar 41, the groove moves to the ride cymbal and the fills that follow lead to the bass solo in section F.

Bars 33–40 | *Guitar solo accompaniment*
You will need to develop the groove according to the style, your personal interpretation and the other instruments used on the backing track. Remember to support the soloist and provide an inspiring foundation for the improvisation.

Bar 40 | *Fill*
When the word fill appears in the notation above any bar with slashed notes, you are free to play your own improvised fill. The fills should be accurate, confident and in keeping with the style of the piece.

E Section (Bars 47–54)
The E section includes a four bar bass solo as well as a four bar drum solo.

Bars 51–54 | *Drum solo*
Drum solos in this style commonly include fast rhythmic patterns moved around the kit. It is natural to speed up when playing exciting and improvised sections, so make sure you keep in time with the track. Blink-182 drummer Travis Barker's playing will provide some inspiration.

G Section (Bars 55–66)
The first eight bars are a reprise of section C. In the following four bars there is a punk tom groove and the choke cymbal technique is introduced.

Bar 63 | *Punk toms*
The quarter-note bass drums can be your anchor here. Work on the phrase played by the hands at a slow tempo and decide which sticking you prefer to use. If you want to keep your right hand on the floor tom, use your left on the snare and medium tom (sticking option 1). Don't compromise the intensity when your right hand plays three consecutive strokes in the middle of the bar. Sticking option 2 will require solid left hand technique (Fig. 2).

Bar 66 | *Choke*
When the word 'choke' appears above a cymbal note, the natural decay of the cymbal must be stopped. This is done by grabbing the cymbal straight after hitting it. An efficient way to do this is to grab the cymbal with the opposite hand to the one used to stroke the cymbal.

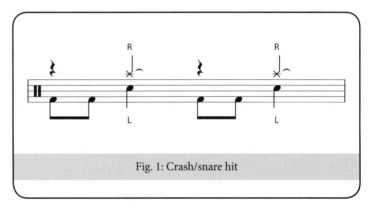

Fig. 1: Crash/snare hit

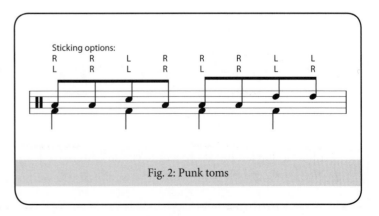

Fig. 2: Punk toms

SONG TITLE: MAIDEN VOYAGE

GENRE: INDIE ROCK

TEMPO: 130 BPM

TECH FEATURES: FLOOR TOM BEATS

16TH NOTE PATTERNS

CRESCENDO

COMPOSER: JOE BENNETT

PERSONNEL: STUART RYAN (GTR)

HENRY THOMAS (BASS)

NOAM LEDERMAN (DRUMS)

JOE BENNETT (KEYS)

OVERVIEW

'Maiden Voyage' tips its hat to bands like The Killers, Interpol and The Bravery, who write under the influence of new wave groups of the late 1970s and early 1980s such as Blondie and The Human League. This piece features low-end tom beats, 16th note patterns and a crescendo among its techniques.

STYLE FOCUS

'Maiden Voyage' features two staple techniques of indie rock drummers: playing a groove on the toms without the use of the hi-hat or ride cymbal, and playing a disco style hi-hat pattern based on 16th notes. The use of the toms adds power to a beat and gives a different feel to the music as the high-frequency metallic sounds of the hi-hats and cymbals are absent. The 16th notes on the hi-hat type groove is a disco classic, although in disco it is commonly played with the bass drum on every downbeat rather than just on the '2' and '4' of the bar as in this song.

THE BIGGER PICTURE

Blondie started life at the iconic venue CBGBs in New York and played straight-ahead new wave rock. By the end of the 1970s Blondie were dabbling in disco on the album *Eat To The Beat* (1979), and then rap on *Autoamerican* (1980). The six-piece first achieved fame in Britain and not their native America, a feat replicated two decades later by Las Vegas' The Killers.

Fronted by Brandon Flowers with the excellent Ronnie Vannucci Jr on drums, The Killers tapped into the vein of dance rock with copious amounts of catchy guitar hooks backed up by dance friendly rhythms. Vannucci has a knack for creating clever drum parts and adding distinctive flourishes to his beats.

RECOMMENDED LISTENING

Two vintage hits that have become cornerstones of the genre are Blondie's 'Atomic' and 'Heart Of Glass', upon which drummer Clem Burke proved twice over that punks could play disco. The Killers' debut, *Hot Fuss* (2004), became a hit thanks to the singles 'Somebody Told Me' and 'All These Things That I've Done', which entered the UK top 20 chart on their release. Vannucci Jr's solo project, *Big Talk* (2001), brings his new wave influences to the fore but tracks like 'Getaways' retain a dance sensibility. For indie rock inspiration listen to 'An Honest Mistake' by The Bravery and Interpol's 'C'mere'.

Maiden Voyage

Joe Bennett

This music is copyright. Photocopying is illegal.

Drums Grade 3

Walkthrough

A Section (Bars 1–8)
This exciting rock beat is played on the snare and toms.

Bar 1 | *Accented toms*
The groove is led by the consistent eighth-note floor toms played with your right hand. Your left hand plays the snare and accented strokes on the high and medium toms. To ensure these accents stand out, lift your hand higher and hit the middle of the drum head with conviction (Fig. 1).

Bar 8 | *Fill*
The two beat fill begins on the third beat of this bar. Following the eighth-note flam, there are six consecutive 16th notes to play on the snare. Use alternate sticking starting with the right and aim to achieve an even, balanced sound.

B Section (Bars 9–16)
In this section the groove moves to the hi-hat with a relatively simple bass and snare drum pattern.

C Section (Bars 17–25)
The first eight bars of this section consist of a 16th note hi-hat rock beat. From bar 22, there are rhythmic stabs and improvised fills to perform.

Bar 17 | *16th note hi-hat groove*
The best way to start working on this type of beat is to play consistent 16th notes on the hi-hat with a metronome until you achieve accuracy. Using the count "1 e & a 2 e & a", move your right hand from the hi-hat to the snare in order to play the backbeat and then move it straight back to continue the 16th note pattern. Aim for a quick, fluent and efficient way of performing this movement (Fig. 2).

Bar 23 | *Fill*
When the word fill appears in the notation above any bar with slashed notes, this means you are free to play your own improvised fill. Fills should be accurate, confident and in keeping with the style of the piece.

D Section (Bars 26–33)
The groove in this section is similar to the B section with more rests and accents on the offbeat of the fourth beat.

Bar 29 | *Closed hi-hat, no bass drum*
By now you are probably used to grooves where the closed hi-hat (following an open one) is played with the bass drum. In this bar, the closed hi-hat is played without the bass drum. Don't let this affect your synchronisation to the backing track. This is a chance to improve your hi-hat foot technique and ensure you are in control of every aspect of it.

E Section (Bars 34–41)
The A section groove is repeated here. From bar 38, you should develop the part stylistically.

Bars 38–41 | *Development*
Treat this as a drum solo that fits what is being played on the track. Remember that any improvised sections need to sound fluent, effortless and convincing.

F Section (Bars 42–54)
The guitar solo fills the first eight bars of this section. Half of this part is notated and the other half is open to your interpretation. In the last five bars, you will return to the toms and build up towards the stabs in the final bar.

Bars 46–49 | *Guitar solo accompaniment*
Remember, the development of the drum part should not affect the flow of time. Keeping your sound production balanced will ensure the guitar solo is not covered by a wall of crashes, open hi-hats and fills.

Bars 50–53 | *Long crescendo*
In these bars, you need to gradually increase the dynamic level over four bars. First, ensure that you start the section at a low dynamic level and then increase the level every bar until you reach bar 54. Secondly, practise the phrase and aim to gradually increase the volume throughout the section. As always, the closer you keep your hand to the surface of the drum the softer the stroke will be.

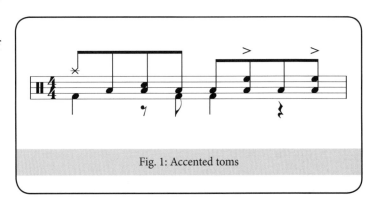

Fig. 1: Accented toms

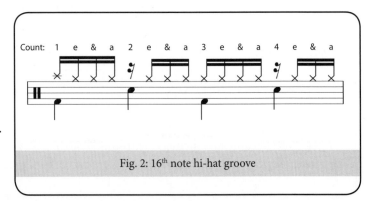

Fig. 2: 16th note hi-hat groove

SONG TITLE: RASTA MONKEY

GENRE: REGGAE

TEMPO: 156 BPM

TECH FEATURES: REGGAE ONE DROP FEEL
SNARE & BASS UNISON
CROSS STICK

COMPOSER: NOAM LEDERMAN

PERSONNEL: STUART RYAN (GTR)
HENRY THOMAS (BASS)
NOAM LEDERMAN (DRUMS)
ROSS STANLEY (KEYS)
FERGUS GERRAND (PERC)

OVERVIEW

The laidback feel of 'Rasta Monkey' recalls the work of reggae legends Bob Marley & The Wailers, Jimmy Cliff and Toots & The Maytals. Its techniques include a one drop feel, an accent on the third beat, and snare and bass played in unison.

STYLE FOCUS

'Rasta Monkey' is an example of the classic one drop style of reggae in which an accent is placed on the third beat of the bar. The space between accents, which is much greater here than in most rock music where the accents fall on the second and third beats of the bar, provides reggae with its smooth, relaxed groove even if the tempo is fast. The snare is often played with a cross-stick and with the bass drum hitting simultaneously to emphasise the third beat.

THE BIGGER PICTURE

In 1968, Toots & The Maytals released a single called 'Do The Reggay'. The word reggay (subsequently written as reggae) came from Jamaican slang and became synonymous with this style of music. Reggae is considered a slower version of rocksteady with rhythm guitar usually playing on the '&-a' of each beat rather than on the '&' only, as was the case with rocksteady and ska. Bob Marley And The Wailers took reggae beyond the shores of Jamaica in 1973 with their hit album *Catch A Fire*, featuring the classic songs 'Stir It Up' and 'Concrete Jungle'. Marley remains reggae's brightest star.

Reggae has produced plenty of accomplished drummers including Carlton Barrett who backed Bob Marley & The Wailers. As one half of the Riddim Twins alongside bassist Robbie Shakespeare, Sly Dunbar has cut albums with everyone from Peter Tosh of The Wailers to producer Lee 'Scratch' Perry.

RECOMMENDED LISTENING

Toots & The Maytals' *Pressure Drop: The Definitive Collection* (2008) features one of the band's signature tunes '54–46 Was My Number' and 'Funky Kingston', a blend of reggae and soul. Marley inspired everyone from Eric Clapton to The Rolling Stones to try their hands at playing reggae – check out *Natty Dread* (1974) and *Exodus* (1977) to hear why. Cliff's album *Jimmy Cliff* (*Wonderful World, Beautiful People*) (1969) included the single 'Many Rivers To Cross', while the song 'The Harder They Come' featured in the Jamaican movie of the same name.

Rasta Monkey

Noam Lederman

Drums Grade 3

Drums Grade 3

Walkthrough

A Section (Bars 1–8)

This section has a reggae groove with accented hi-hats and snare cross stick. It starts in bar 1, following a pick-up fill.

Pick up bar | *Counting the pick-up*

In this piece, there is a two beat pick-up fill before the groove begins in bar 1. The first snare stroke is placed on the third beat in the second bar of the spoken count in. There are no other instruments that play this pattern, so use the backing track and your inner pulse.

Bar 1 | *Cross stick*

The cross stick technique is common in reggae and used in many other styles of drumming. In order to perform it, place the palm of your left hand on the snare drum head and strike the rim with the stick. Ensure that part of your palm remains in contact with the drum head because removing your hand before each stroke will affect the sound produced. Before attempting the full groove, practise this technique and find the area of the rim where the cross stick sounds balanced and rounded (known as the sweet spot) (Fig. 1).

Bar 1 | *Hi-hat accents*

Accent the second and fourth hi-hat notes in this bar. These accented and non-accented hi-hats are vital to the fluency of the reggae groove. You can achieve this by lifting your stick higher when performing an accent and keeping it closer when attempting an unaccented stroke.

Bar 2 | *Hi-hat triplet*

In this bar, the hi-hat pattern develops with a quarter note and eight-note triplet on the fourth beat. This means that the second part of this triplet will not be played. Keep your timing accurate and the accent audible.

B Section (Bars 9–24)

The reggae groove here is similar to the previous one but with some added stylistic fills.

Bar 12 | *Triplet fill*

Triplets are most commonly counted as "1-trip-let 2-trip-let". Whatever you decide to use to count the triplet, remember that you are aiming to achieve three even strokes in the space of one quarter note. The counting for this specific fill is "1-trip-let 2-(rest)-let 3-(rest)-let 4" and the suggested sticking is R L R L (snare) and R L R L (floor tom). Make sure that the sound produced from the kit is not affected by the challenging rhythm here (Fig. 2).

C Section (Bars 25–40)

The groove develops with quarter-note bass drum, snare and improvised fills.

Bars 26–27 | *Snare/cross stick change*

In these bars, you need to change from snare to cross stick without stopping the groove. Practise this change separately at first and aim to use the most straightforward and efficient movement. After you are able to play both sounds in time, focus upon finding the sweet spot of the cross stick under pressure. Memorising your hand position on the snare when achieving the ideal cross stick sound will help when you play along with the track.

Bar 32 | *Fill*

When the word fill appears in the notation above a bar with slashed notes, you are free to play your own improvised fill. Fills should be performed accurately and be in keeping with the style of the piece.

D & E Sections (bars 41–52)

Section D is an eight bar guitar solo. Section E is the reprise of section B. The final bars are those marked 'Coda'.

Bars 43–48 | *Guitar solo accompaniment*

Develop the groove according to the style, your personal interpretation and the other instruments used on the backing track. The development created by the drums is meant to support the soloist and provide an exciting foundation for the improvisation.

Bars 50–51 | *Crescendo*

Apply a crescendo and gradually get louder in these bars.

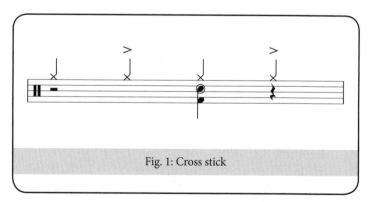

Fig. 1: Cross stick

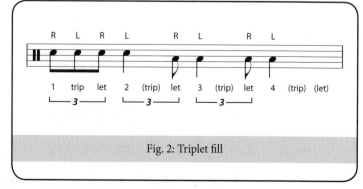

Fig. 2: Triplet fill

SONG TITLE: FALLOUT

GENRE: METAL

TEMPO: 75 BPM

TECH FEATURES: DOUBLE TIME
SYNCOPATED PUSHES
16TH NOTE FILLS

COMPOSERS: JASON BOWLD
& CHARLIE GRIFFITHS

PERSONNEL: CHARLIE GRIFFITHS (GTR)
HENRY THOMAS (BASS)
NOAM LEDERMAN (DRUMS)

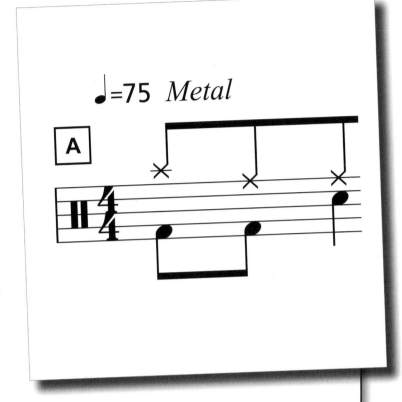

OVERVIEW

'Fallout' is a heavy sludge metal style track inspired by bands like Black Sabbath, Soundgarden and Down. It features double time, syncopated pushes and 16th note fills among its techniques.

STYLE FOCUS

Sludge metal needs to be played with conviction to sound heavy because of its slower than average tempo. This slower tempo does allow for more interesting syncopated grooves and accents, though, and because it is slower it usually grooves more. Any fills that run in unison with guitar riffs need to be locked in with the guitars to create the power needed to back up the steady grooving that the track carries. Being in control of the tempo is crucial to achieving a big sound.

THE BIGGER PICTURE

Sludge or sludge metal refers to bands who were influenced by the slow, gloomy grooves and subtle blues influences of Black Sabbath. In the 1980s, hardcore punk band the Melvins discovered the power of performing grooves at a slow tempo as opposed to the frantic punk thrashing that was popular at the time. Soundgarden released their debut, *Ultramega OK*, in 1988 and demonstrated a love of Black Sabbath style slow grooves combined with psychedelia and odd-time signature riffs.

In the 1990s, the metal supergroup Down, which comprised members of Pantera and Corrosion Of Conformity, came to epitomise the sludge metal sound with down-tuned guitars and aggressive vocals.

Although they are most often cited as stoner rock, the Californian group Kyuss also displayed elements of sludge in their sound.

RECOMMENDED LISTENING

The early Black Sabbath albums *Black Sabbath* (1970), *Paranoid* (1970) and *Masters Of Reality* (1971) were key to the development of sludge metal. 'Sweet Leaf', 'War Pigs' and 'Iron Man' are the roots of sludge metal. *NOLA* (1995) and *Down III: Over The Under* (2007) by Down continued the tradition as their drummer Jimmy Bower followed in the footsteps of Sabbath's Bill Ward. *Badmotorfinger* (1991) and *Superunknown* (1994) by Soundgarden boasted tasteful playing from Matt Cameron (who also plays in Pearl Jam). 'Jesus Christ Pose' and 'Black Hole Sun' are classic examples of grunge's sludge tendencies.

Fallout

Jason Bowld & Charlie Griffiths

Drums Grade 3

Walkthrough

A Section (Bars 1–8)
Section A has a steady groove with syncopated snares. The backbeat is missing from beat two of every other bar. Play around it with various fills to mirror the guitar riff.

Bar 1 | *Main groove*
Although reasonably straight, the main groove features a syncopated snare that is played after beat three. Try counting the following rhythm to help you maintain good timing: "1& 2& 3e& 4e&" (Fig. 1). This main groove is played in bars 1, 3, 5 and 7.

Bar 2 | *Syncopated snares*
This bar, which serves as an answer to the main groove, is repeated to some extent in bars 2, 4, 6 and 8, some of which feature slightly different tails on beats three and four. The syncopated snares have a similar feel to the main groove except they play either side of beat two.

B Section (Bars 9–12)
This section features a heavy 4/4 groove with a fill that leads into the guitar solo.

Bars 9–11 | *Straight groove*
If you feel as though you are rushing the groove here, focus on your sound and how you hit the drums. This should steady your timing.

Bar 12 | *Fill to B section*
The two crashes played on beats three and four are important because they emphasise the guitar chords, so let them be your focus for this fill.

C section – development (Bars 13–16)
Now is your chance to embellish and develop the main groove from the A section with different fills. Because it is a guitar solo section, you can use the ride cymbal to mirror the dynamics of the guitar. Any fills should complement the guitar riff's accents.

D Section (Bars 17–28)
Musically, this section is the same as the B section except this time the rhythms intensify and evolve into a double time feel halfway through.

Bars 17–19 | *Extra bass drums*
You will notice here that the main difference between this groove and the straight groove played in the B section is the addition of two extra bass drums played on '3 &' and '4 e'. These two bass hits emphasise the guitar riff and will make it easier to lock down the timing.

Bars 21–27 | *Double time groove*
'Double time' indicates that the written drum part in this section will be played twice as fast. This is also referred to as 'cut time' or 'Alla breve'. The double time groove emphasises the guitar riff with the bass drums. Note that the bass on beat three is missing from every other bar.

E Section (Bars 29–36)
The double time feel continues here but with the groove developing with the music and also allowing room to add your own embellishments.

Bars 29–36 | *Double time groove expansions*
The double time groove now expands alongside the guitar riff. Starting with a regular groove in bar 29, this alternates with different patterns that follow the guitar. In bar 30, the rhythm counts as "1& &3 4&" (see Fig. 2). Further development of the groove must be appropriate stylistically in bars 33–35.

F Section (Bars 37–41)
In this final section you will return to the original drum feel. These last five bars are a reprise of the A section, except in bar 40 where you play a unison eighth-note triplet fill on the snare and floor tom which leads to the final crash in bar 41. Count the triplet fill "3-trip-let 4-trip-let" to help maintain accurate timing.

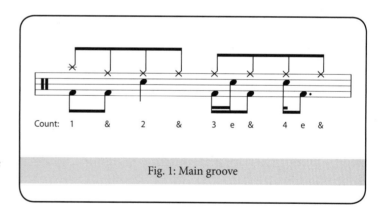

Fig. 1: Main groove

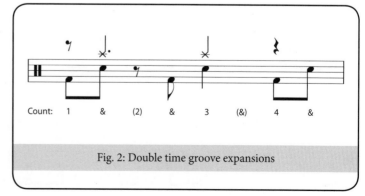

Fig. 2: Double time groove expansions

Technical Exercises

In this section the examiner will ask you to play a selection of exercises drawn from each of the five groups shown below. In addition there is a Fill exercise which you will play using the designated backing track. You do not need to memorise the exercises (and can use the book in the exam) but the examiner will be looking for the speed of your response.

The stickings shown (L & R) are there as a guide for right handed drummers. Left handed drummers should reverse the sticking patterns. Before you start the section you will be asked whether you would like to play the exercises along with the click or hear a single bar of click before you commence the test. Groups A–E should be played at ♩=75.

Group A: Single Strokes
Single strokes in eighth notes, eighth note triplets and 16th notes

Group B: Double Strokes
Double strokes in eighth and 16th notes, using snare and toms

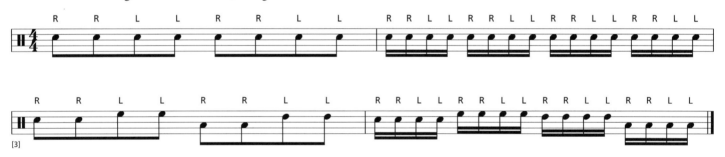

Group C: Paradiddles
Single paradiddle in 16th notes with accents on snare and toms

Group D: Flams and Drags

Flams and drags in quarter notes

Group E: Triplets

Triplets in eighth notes with accents on snare and toms

Group F: Fill

In the exam you will be asked to play the three bar groove shown followed by one of the notated fills chosen by the examiner. The fills consist of alternating eighth notes, triplet eighth notes, 16th notes and flams. The snare is to be played as a cross stick. You will perform this exercise to the backing track. The tempo is ♩ = 80.

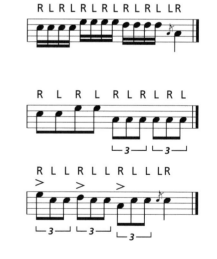

Sight Reading

In this section you have a choice between either a sight reading test or an improvisation & interpretation test (see facing page). You will be asked to prepare a sight reading test which will be given to you by the examiner. The test is four bars long and played on the snare drum. The examiner will allow you 90 seconds to prepare it and will set the tempo for you. The tempo is ♩ = 70–80.

Improvisation & Interpretation

You will be asked to play a written one bar groove, vary it in the following two bars and improvise a fill in the fourth bar. The test will be played to a backing track using the bass drum, hi-hat (closed and open), snare drum, ride cymbal and crash cymbal. You have 30 seconds to prepare then you will be allowed to practise during the first playing of the backing track, before playing it to the examiner on the second playing of the backing track. This test is continuous with a one bar count-in at the beginning and after the practice session. The tempo is ♩=80–100.

Ear Tests

There are two ear tests in this grade. The examiner will play each test to you twice. You will find one example of each type of test printed below.

Test 1: Fill Playback and Recognition

The examiner will play you a one bar fill in common time played on the snare drum. You will play back the fill on the snare drum. You will then identify the fill from two printed examples shown to you by the examiner. You will hear the test twice.

Each time the test is played it is preceded by a one bar count in. There will be a short gap for you to practise. Next you will hear the vocal count in and you will then play the fill to the click. The tempo is ♩= 70.

Test 2: Groove Recall

The examiner will play you a two-bar groove played on the bass drum, hi-hat (open and closed), crash cymbal and snare. This is a two bar groove repeated. You will hear the test twice. You will be asked to play the groove back on the drum voices indicated for four bars.

Each time the test is played it is preceded by a one bar vocal count-in. The tempo is ♩= 80.

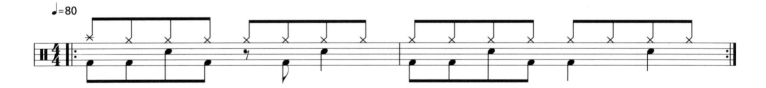

General Musicianship Questions

In this part of the exam you will be asked five questions. Four of these questions will be about general music knowledge and the fifth question will be asked about your instrument.

Music Knowledge

The examiner will ask you four music knowledge questions based on a piece of music that you have played in the exam. You will nominate the piece of music about which the questions will be asked.

In Grade 3, you will be asked:

- Drum voices on the stave

- The meaning of the time signature marking

- Quarter, dotted eighth note, eighth note, triplet eighth note and 16th note values

- Rest values

- Repeat markings including first and second time bars

Instrument Knowledge

The examiner will also ask you one question regarding your instrument.

In Grade 3 you will be asked to identify:

- The following parts of the drum kit – bass drum, snare, high tom, medium tom, floor tom, hi-hat, ride cymbal and crash cymbal

- The following parts of the drumstick – tip, neck, shaft and butt

- Two main drum kit makes

- Two main cymbal makes

Further Information

Tips on how to approach this part of this exam can be found in the *Syllabus Guide* for Drums, the Rockschool *Drums Companion Guide* and on the Rockschool website: *www.rslawards.com*.

Entering Rockschool Exams

Entering a Rockschool exam is easy, just go online and follow our simple six step process. All details for entering online, dates, fees, regulations and Free Choice pieces can be found at *www.rslawards.com*

- All candidates should ensure they bring their own Grade syllabus book to the exam or have proof of digital purchase ready to show the examiner.

- All Grade 6–8 candidates must ensure that they bring valid photo ID to their exam.

Marking Schemes

ELEMENT	PASS	MERIT	DISTINCTION
Performance Piece 1	12–14 out of 20	15–17 out of 20	18+ out of 20
Performance Piece 2	12–14 out of 20	15–17 out of 20	18+ out of 20
Performance Piece 3	12–14 out of 20	15–17 out of 20	18+ out of 20
Technical Exercises	9–10 out of 15	11–12 out of 15	13+ out of 15
Sight Reading *or* Improvisation & Interpretation	6 out of 10	7–8 out of 10	9+ out of 10
Ear Tests	6 out of 10	7–8 out of 10	9+ out of 10
General Musicianship Questions	3 out of 5	4 out of 5	5 out of 5
TOTAL MARKS	60%+	74%+	90%+

GRADE EXAMS | GRADES 6–8

ELEMENT	PASS	MERIT	DISTINCTION
Performance Piece 1	12–14 out of 20	15–17 out of 20	18+ out of 20
Performance Piece 2	12–14 out of 20	15–17 out of 20	18+ out of 20
Performance Piece 3	12–14 out of 20	15–17 out of 20	18+ out of 20
Technical Exercises	9–10 out of 15	11–12 out of 15	13+ out of 15
Quick Study Piece	6 out of 10	7–8 out of 10	9+ out of 10
Ear Tests	6 out of 10	7–8 out of 10	9+ out of 10
General Musicianship Questions	3 out of 5	4 out of 5	5 out of 5
TOTAL MARKS	60%+	74%+	90%+

PERFORMANCE CERTIFICATES | DEBUT TO GRADE 8 *

ELEMENT	PASS	MERIT	DISTINCTION
Performance Piece 1	12–14 out of 20	15–17 out of 20	18+ out of 20
Performance Piece 2	12–14 out of 20	15–17 out of 20	18+ out of 20
Performance Piece 3	12–14 out of 20	15–17 out of 20	18+ out of 20
Performance Piece 4	12–14 out of 20	15–17 out of 20	18+ out of 20
Performance Piece 5	12–14 out of 20	15–17 out of 20	18+ out of 20
TOTAL MARKS	60%+	75%+	90%+

* Note that there are no Debut Vocal exams.

Drums Notation Explained

BASS DRUM & TOMS

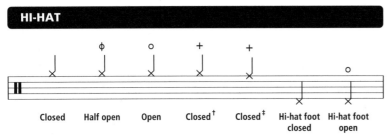

Bass drum   Floor tom   Medium tom   High tom

SNARE

Snare   Ghost snare   Rim-shot   Cross stick   Buzz snare

Strike snare drum and surrounding rim at same time   *Place palm on snare drum head and strike rim with stick*

HI-HAT

Closed   Half open   Open   Closed †   Closed ‡   Hi-hat foot closed   Hi-hat foot open

† *Used on the first closed hi-hat that follows an open hi-hat*

‡ *The hi-hat is closed without being struck. Note that the hi-hat closed (cross) symbol may appear above drum voices other than the hi-hat (as shown above). This simply means another drum voice is being played at the same moment that the hi-hat is being closed.*

OTHER CYMBALS

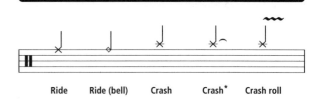

Ride   Ride (bell)   Crash   Crash*   Crash roll

Allow all cymbals to ring on *unless explicitly stopped, as indicated by the keyword* *'Choke'*. *Occasionally ties may be used (*) to emphasise that cymbals should be allowed to ring on. This can avoid confusion during syncopations and pushes.*

GENERAL MUSIC NOTATION

Accentuate note (play it louder).

D.%. al Coda

Go back to the sign (%) then play until the bar marked **To Coda** ⊕ then skip to the section marked ⊕ **Coda**.

D.C. al Fine

Go back to beginning of song and play until bar marked **Fine** (end).

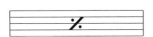

Repeat the previous bar. In higher grades these may also be marked *sim.* or *cont. sim.*

In rudiments, each stem slash subdivides the note value by half.

Slashes are used to demarcate bars during solos, fills, developments and other ad lib. sections.

Repeat the bars between the repeat signs.

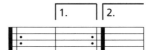

When a repeated section has different endings, play the first ending only the first time and the second ending only the second time.

Repeat the previous two bars. In higher grades these may also be marked *sim.* or *cont. sim.*

MUSICAL TERMS WITH SPECIFIC EXAMINATION DEFINITIONS

Fill   Play an individual, stylistic fill.

Cont. sim.   Continue in similar way but vary the pattern slightly.

Develop   Extend the musical part in a stylistically appropriate manner.

Rit. (ritardando)   Gradually slow the tempo.

SONG TITLE: THE NOD

GENRE: HIP HOP

TEMPO: 95 BPM

TECH FEATURES: 16TH-NOTE GROOVES & FILLS
CROSS STICK
RIM-SHOTS

COMPOSER: NEEL DHORAJIWALA

PERSONNEL: NEEL DHORAJIWALA (PROD)
NOAM LEDERMAN (DRUMS)
FERGUS GERRAND (PERC)
HENRY THOMAS (BASS)
HARRY LOVE (DJ)

OVERVIEW

'The Nod' is a hip hop track in the style of artists from America's East Coast such as The Roots, Nas and Gang Starr. It features cross stick, rim-shots as well as 16th-note grooves and fills among its techniques.

STYLE FOCUS

Unlike gangsta rap, which employed live musicians in many of its recordings, East Coast hip hop was produced traditionally using drum machines and samplers. However, many hip hop acts prefer to use live drums onstage. The result is a human groove coupled with a machine-like feel and approach to the drum part. Emulating the straight quantization of a drum machine or the swing feel of an Akai MPC sampler might sound like a simple task, but actually achieving a balance of human and drum machine feel is a difficult skill to master.

THE BIGGER PICTURE

Hip hop was created in New York in the late 1970s and spread across America's East Coast in the early 1980s. East Coast hip hop is characterised by heavy beats programmed on drum machines, like Akai's

MPC, and by its creative use of samples. Purists consider it to be the original, and therefore best, form of hip hop. However, that's not to say disciples of this sound are limited by its original parameters. Philadelphia's The Roots, for example, have embraced live musicianship as a way of extending the dynamic range in the live arena and as a nod to the original artists who were sampled by hip hop producers.

As well as performing under their own banner, The Roots have played a supporting role to numerous hip hop artists including Jay Z, Kanye West and Common. The band's drummer Amir 'Questlove' Thompson is the foremost drummer within the hip hop genre.

Chris 'Daddy' Dave is another excellent hip hop drummer. His ability to find a groove somewhere between straight quantization and heavy swing makes him an ideal player to learn from.

RECOMMENDED LISTENING

For classic East Coast drum programming listen to Nas' debut album *Illmatic* (1993). Also, the hip hop duos Pete Rock & CL Smooth's *The Main Ingredient* (1994) and Gang Starr's *Daily Operation* (1992) are strong examples from that period. Lastly, The Roots are best sampled via *How I Got Over* (2010).

The Nod (Grade 4 Preview)

Neel Dhorajiwala

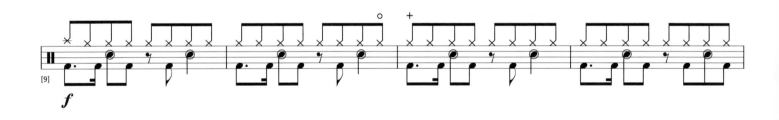

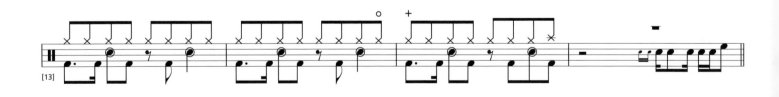

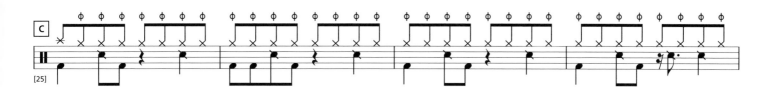

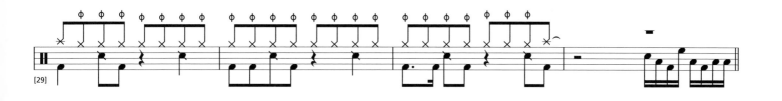

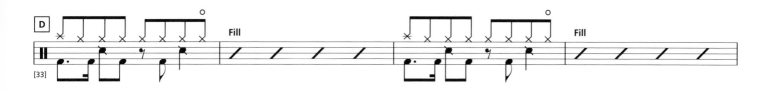

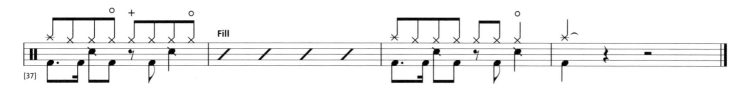

Drums Grade 3

41

Walkthrough (Grade 4 Preview)

A Section (Bars 1–16)
This section features a hip hop beat with eighth-note hi-hats, cross stick backbeat and a varied bass drum pattern. The syncopated crash push in bar 15 and the fill in bar 16 prepare for the groove change in section B.

Bar 1 | *Cross stick*
The cross stick technique is common in hip hop but is used in many other styles too. To perform this technique, place the palm of your left hand on the snare drum head and strike the rim with your stick. Ensure that part of your palm remains in contact with the drum head because removing your hand before each stroke will affect the sound produced. Before attempting the full groove, practise this technique and find the area of the rim where the cross stick sounds most balanced and rounded. This area is known as the sweet spot. When playing a whole section using the cross stick, some drummers choose to use the 'butt' part of the drum stick because it produces a more defined sound.

Bar 4 | *Advanced co-ordination*
Co-ordinating the bottom part of the stave pattern with the hi-hats is one of the biggest challenges of this piece. Practise the cross stick/bass drum pattern without the hi-hat and ensure that all the rhythmic values are accurate. When adding the hi-hat pattern, pay attention to the pulse and work on achieving fluency within it.

Bar 16 | *Drag fill*
There are two beats of rest following the syncopated crash at the end of bar 15. The first snare stroke on beat three should be played with a drag, which means performing both grace notes before the main stroke. Use the natural bounce of the stick and a firm but not too tight grip in order to achieve accurate and fluent grace notes. The suggested sticking for this fill is shown in Fig. 1.

B Section (Bars 17–24)
Here the second main groove is introduced. This hip hop groove is based on 16th-note hi-hats using alternate sticking. From bar 18, you can develop the drum part stylistically. Make sure that you do so in keeping with the genre.

C Section (Bars 25–32)
The drum pattern intensifies in this section, with rim-shot snare and half open hi-hat.

Bar 25 | *Rim-shot*
The rim-shot technique is an integral part of drumming and is used in many styles. To produce a rim-shot you must strike the snare drum and surrounding rim at the same time. This will produce a louder and more pronounced sound.

The rim-shot should become a natural technique for you which can be performed on demand at any time. If you struggle to produce the rim-shot, try changing the height of your snare drum and the angle until you reach the position that suits you most (Fig. 2).

Bar 25 | *Half open hi-hat*
The vertical line through the open hi-hat mark indicates that the hi-hat should be only half open in this section. This can be done by tightening your hi-hat foot on the pedal. Ideally, the hi-hat cymbals will be consistently close to each other and produce a sizzling sound.

Bars 32 | *16th notes around the kit*
Two advanced approaches to fills are used here: dividing the strokes into uneven groups and using combinations of hands and feet. Practising this fill at a slower tempo will allow your body to learn and internalise the movement. The logical sticking pattern to use in this fill is L R F L R F R L (foot/bass drum marked as F). This combination of R L and L R lead follows the set-up of drums and allows you to develop further your control around the kit. Experiment with different stickings and move the fill around the kit in order to internalise the movement and rhythms.

D Section (Bars 33–40)
Now you have the opportunity to display your technical ability and understanding of the style. Listening to hip hop drummers such as The Roots' Ahmir 'Questlove' Thompson and Chris 'Daddy' Dave will give you ideas for improvised fills in this style.

Fig. 1: Drag fill

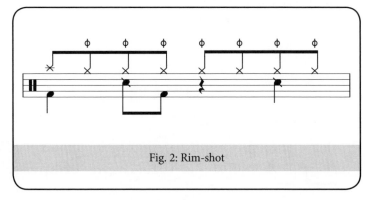

Fig. 2: Rim-shot

rockschool®

DIGITAL DOWNLOADS NOW AVAILABLE!

All your favourite Rockschool titles are now available to download instantly from the RSL shop. Download entire grade books, individual tracks or supporting tests to all your devices.

START DOWNLOADING NOW

www.rslawards.com/shop

INTRODUCING...

rockschool®

POPULAR MUSIC THEORY

The *essential* guide for rock & pop musicians

GRADES DEBUT–8

For ROCKSCHOOL'S NEW THEORY EXAMS!

OUT NOW!

Discover more at
www.rslawards.com/theory

Enter online at
www.rslawards.com/enter-online